The Plight Beneath
The Northern Light

The Right to Meet and Form Groups

Written by Dustin Milligan • Illustrated by Cory Tibbits

DC Canada Education Publishing

Written by: Dustin Milligan

Illustrated by: Cory Tibbits

Editor: Leonard Judge

Copy Editor: Anja Pujic

Cover Design: Meredith Luce

Published in 2012 by: DC Canada Education Publishing

130 Slater Street, Suite 960
Ottawa, On, Canada K1P 6E2
www.dc-canada.ca

. . . .

**We acknowledge the financial support of the Government of Canada
through the Canada Book Fund for our publishing activities.**

The Plight Beneath the Northern Light

ISBN: 978-1-926776-36-1

. . . .

Library and Archives Canada Cataloguing in Publication
Milligan, Dustin, 1984-
The plight beneath the northern light : the right to meet and form groups with friends,
neighbours and family / written by Dustin Milligan ; illustrated by Cory Tibbits.
(The charter for children)
Includes bibliographical references.
ISBN 978-1-926776-36-1
1. Freedom of association--Canada--Juvenile literature.
2. Assembly, Right of--Canada--Juvenile literature.
I. Tibbits, Cory II. Title. III. Series: Charter for children
KE4425.M55 2012   j323.4'70971   C2012-901834-1

Preface

. . . .

The idea for *The Charter for Children* first emerged when I was a student at the Faculty of Law at McGill University. After my first year of studies, I was concerned that the common citizen wasn't equipped to understand our country's complicated legal system—one that I myself had only begun to comprehend. Children are at a further disadvantage in this regard, as they have limited capacity, strength and knowledge of their rights. Combining these concerns with my love for literature and the law, I took on this large project—writing a series of books that offer children a basic understanding of the *Canadian Charter of Rights and Freedoms*. Thus *The Charter for Children* was born.

I would like to thank the Faculty of Law at McGill University, and most notably, Professor Shauna Van Praagh, who provided guidance during the majority of this project and without whom the project would not have been possible. I would also like to thank those who have contributed their thoughts, insights, encouragement, time, and puns—most notably, my three friends, Dorian Needham, Malcolm Dort, and Josie Marks, as well as the wonderful team at DC Canada Education Publishing, Rachel Doran, Pippa McIntyre, Rina Jeyakumar, Megan Howatt, Meagan Johnston, and my incredible family, Keith, Deborah, Olivia, Christian, and Jolene.

This series is dedicated to the children of Canada—may your voices be heard and considered, and may your childhood be filled with respect and dignity.

Dustin Milligan

In a time not so long ago, on the ice of Hudson Bay in Nunavut, there lived a polar bear named Iqsituittuq.

Iqsi was worried.

The Polar Oil Company had discovered oil beneath the ice of her hometown. The company was going to start drilling into the ice to get the oil out.

The company would bring lots of toonies to her hometown. And the polar bears loved toonies—especially since their picture was on them!

But getting the oil out would also cause great problems for the environment.

Iqsi learned that Mayor Angajuqqausikkaq (Angajuq, for short) had arranged the deal with the Polar Oil Company all by himself. He hadn't discussed it with any of the bears on Hudson Bay.

Iqsi wanted to gather her community together to discuss the company's plans. She wanted to make sure that the environment was going to be safe and clean.

But this was no easy task.

Mayor Angajuq was a clever mayor. He didn't want the community to meet with the Polar Oil Company. He was more interested in making lots of toonies than in protecting the environment. So he pretended that the ice would break if too many bears gathered on it at once.

He posted the Two-Bears Rule on the town's largest iceberg in the centre of Hudson Bay.

It read:

> *To ensure safety of all bears on the bay,*
> *And to prevent the ice from giving way,*
> *There is a new rule that all bears must obey:*
>
> *Bears are restricted to groups of two.*
> *The Polar Police are watching you!*
> *If you gather with more bears at one time,*
> *Your fur will be shaved and you will be fined!*

The Two-Bears Rule was causing major problems.

One day, Iqsi's best friend Piqan invited three pals to his iglu. They sat around playing a game of Trivial Fursuit.

Piqan asked his friend:

> *What is the oldest company in Canada?*

Before his friend could respond, there was a knock on the door.

The Polar Police entered.

The Polar Police arrested all four bears. They fined the bears two toonies each and shaved off all their fur.

The chief of police said:

You know the rule.
Bears can only meet in a pair!
You broke the law.
Now you'll freeze with no hair!

Even some members of the Polar Police were concerned about the harsh Two-Bears Rule.

The chief of police asked the mayor if he would reconsider the rule.

But the mayor said:

> *I'm the mayor! I won the election!*
> *The police are under my direction!*
> *In order to make lots of loonies and toonies,*
> *We need the rule to prevent objection!*

And so the Polar Oil Company began to build giant drills.

Mayor Angajuq welcomed the Polar Oil Company as it grew bigger and bigger. Soon the company would start drilling holes in the centre of Iqsi's hometown.

And they hadn't discussed the plans with anyone but the mayor!

Mayor Angajuq stood on the large iceberg and reminded the bears:

To ensure safety of all bears on the bay,
And to prevent the ice from giving way,
There is a new rule that all bears must obey:

Bears are restricted to groups of two.
The Polar Police are watching you!
If you gather with more bears at one time,
Your fur will be shaved and you will be fined!

After the drilling began, all the bears in town became very worried about the problems the company was causing to the environment.

The polar bears had a tradition of going out on the land, where they hunted and fished to feed their families. They often sat on the edge of the ice with their long fishing rods to catch fresh salmon. Salmon was one of their favourite foods.

One day, while they were fishing, a bear reeled in a nice big salmon. But the salmon was shiny and black. When the bear touched the salmon's skin, he discovered that it was covered in oil!

The location of the drilling was also causing complications for the annual dogsled race—the Hudson Bay Quest.

The race took the same route every year—from Churchill all the way to Arviat.

With the Polar Oil Company drilling in the middle of Hudson Bay, bears competing in the race would have to take a long detour.

One day, Iqsi went figure skating on the ice. It was a beautiful day and the ice was shining. But when Iqsi attempted to twirl, she fell flat on her tail. There was oil all over the ice!

With anger, she shouted:

We bears must do something and do it quick!
Nanook is a crook and it's making me sick!

Iqsi decided to meet with her friend Piqan at Tim Hudson's.

As she drank her iced coffee, she said:

> *Oh Piqan, look what happened to your fleece!*
> *You gathered with friends but met the police!*
> *This town is in so much trouble-trouble.*
> *I think I need another double-double!*

Piqan took a sip of his coffee to keep him warm.

He said to Iqsi:

> We must find a way, for all bears on the bay,
> To meet and band together.
> We must stay strong, and think hard and long,
> Of something very clever!

They both knew that only a large group of bears could challenge the mayor and his plans for the community.

Iqsi and Piqan sat and wondered.

On the television, Sheila Patte-Cloutier was speaking about global warming. As Iqsi watched, she was inspired.

She said:

> We can lift up our paw, without breaking the law,
> If we meet in groups of two.
> While we meet in pairs, we can tell all the bears,
> To meet at a time on cue.
>
> If we're all together, it won't matter whether,
> The chief of police is in view.
> With so many of us, demanding what's just,
> There'll be nothing that they can do!

That day, Iqsi and Piqan put their plan in action.

They met in pairs with all of their friends, neighbours, and family members.

Iqsi visited her neighbour Inuuqati and said:

> *This town must form an association!*
> *We need to express our frustration!*
> *Join our group! It's grave as can be!*
> *We must meet and speak with the Company!*

Piqan visited his Aunt Atsamaaq and said:

We need to gather! This is your warning!
To save our bay! Or we'll be mourning!
Please sign here and every bear on the bay,
Can meet with the mayor without delay!

By meeting in groups of two, Iqsi and Piqan spoke with all of their friends, neighbours, and family members.

Almost every bear on the bay agreed to join the new group. They called themselves *Greenfleece*.

The members of Greenfleece agreed to gather at *katimavik*—the "meeting place"—on the following day.

The next day, the members of Greenfleece met in the centre of town. Iqsi had finally achieved her goal of bringing her friends, neighbours, and family members together.

As they gathered, Iqsi and the bears of Greenfleece worked together to write a new rhyme for the iceberg.

The Polar Police simply stood by and watched. There were too many bears to control!

When the rhyme was finished, Iqsi tore down the Two-Bears Rule.

She replaced it with a new rhyme that read:

We are Greenfleece and demand a say,
In our environment and our bay!
All bears have joined hands, with stands and demands,
To save these lands from the mayor's hidden plans!

Mayor Angajuq was shocked. Almost the entire community had gathered together. They hadn't fallen for his tricks.

In fact, even the chief of police had decided to join Greenfleece!

With his paws in the air, the mayor said:

> *You're right. You're right. I see your plight!*
> *I've finally seen the northern light!*
> *The community must have a say in our bay,*
> *We must work together without delay!*

Soon thereafter, Mayor Angajuq planned a meeting to discuss the town's concerns. Representatives from the Polar Oil Company discussed their plans with members of Greenfleece.

Together they hoped to find a solution for the good of the whole community.

The mayor even served Tim Hudson's coffee. Iqsi raised her cup in the air and said:

Raise your cup to the bears of Hudson Bay!
Together we're stronger, and for all the days longer,
No bear or mayor can stand in our way!

Note for Parents and Teachers:

This story seeks to teach children about the freedoms of assembly and association, which are guaranteed by sections 2(c) and 2(d) of the *Canadian Charter of Rights and Freedoms*. These sections provide that:

> *Everyone has the following fundamental freedoms... (c) freedom of peaceful assembly; and (d) freedom of association.*[1]

Freedom of association provides individuals with the right to establish, to belong to, and to maintain an organization. Freedom of assembly is closely linked to freedom of association and provides individuals with the right to meet as members of a group or organization. The essence of these freedoms was captured by John Stuart Mill who wrote: "From the liberty of each individual follows the liberty, within the same limits of combination among individuals; freedom to unite, for any purpose not involving harm to others."[2]

There are many historical accounts where the freedoms to assemble and associate have been restricted in order to silence opposition. In Canada, such a restriction was imposed in Quebec with "An Act to protect the Province against Communistic Propaganda" in 1937. The law sought to control communism by restricting persons from meeting in houses to propagate communism or bolshevism.[3] More recent debates have arisen in the context of labour relations and have challenged the ability of employees to form unions, to bargain collectively, and to strike.

In this story, the Two-Bears Rule sought to eliminate dissenting opinions in Iqsi's community. Forming organizations or meeting with more than two bears at one time was made illegal. When meetings were forbidden, the bears were unable to voice their opinions and form an effective opposition to the mayor's plans for the community. Iqsi's formation of Greenfleece (an association) and the meeting of the bears by the giant iceberg (an assembly) demonstrate the power of associating and assembling. The community is stronger when it is united as a collective. It is finally able to challenge the mayor's strict control of the town.

Finally, it should be noted that the freedoms of assembly and association are closely related to freedom of expression. Suppressing the freedoms of assembly and association can also suppress a collective's ability to express itself, thereby infringing upon freedom of expression. See *A Portrait of the Artist as a Young Lobster* for a demonstration of this overlap.

Questions for children:

1. What is the Two-Bears Rule? Why did the mayor create the Two-Bears Rule?

2. Why did Iqsi and Piqan organize a group of bears from their community (Greenfleece)?

3. Why couldn't the mayor stop Greenfleece from protesting?

4. Why is the ability to meet and form groups important?

---

[1] *Canadian Charter of Rights and Freedoms*, s 2(c) & 2(d), Part I of the *Constitution Act, 1982*, being Schedule B to the *Canada Act 1982* (UK), 1982, c 11.

[2] The Constitutional Law Group, *Canadian Constitutional Law*, 3rd ed (Toronto: Emond Montgomery Publications Ltd, 2003) at 1031.

[3] *Switzman v Elbling*, [1957] SCR 285, 7 DLR (2d) 337.